# WORD FAMILIES - LONG VOWELS
## Literacy Skills Series

Written by Staci Marck

## GRADE K-1

**Classroom Complete Press**
P.O. Box 19729
San Diego, CA 92159
Tel: 1-800-663-3609 | Fax: 1-800-663-3608
Email: service@classroomcompletepress.com

**www.classroomcompletepress.com**

ISBN-13: 978-1-55319-403-3
ISBN-10: 1-55319-403-9

© 2008

# Critical Thinking Skills

## Word Families - Long Vowels Grade K-1

| Skills For Critical Thinking | Onset-Rime Addition | Make-a-Word | Picture Rimes | Sentence Completion | Cloze | Find-A-Rime | Reading Passages | What's Different? | Writing Tasks | Graphic Organizers |
|---|---|---|---|---|---|---|---|---|---|---|
| **LEVEL 1 Remembering** | | | | | | | | | | |
| • Identify | ✓ | | ✓ | ✓ | | ✓ | ✓ | ✓ | | |
| • Read | ✓ | ✓ | ✓ | ✓ | ✓ | ✓ | ✓ | ✓ | ✓ | ✓ |
| • Match | | ✓ | ✓ | | | | | | | |
| • Select | | ✓ | ✓ | ✓ | | | | | | |
| • Record | ✓ | ✓ | ✓ | ✓ | ✓ | | | | | |
| **LEVEL 2 Understanding** | | | | | | | | | | |
| • Use | ✓ | | ✓ | ✓ | ✓ | ✓ | | ✓ | ✓ | ✓ |
| • Describe | | | | | | | | | | |
| • Interpret | | | | | | | | ✓ | | |
| **LEVEL 3 Applying** | | | | | | | | | | |
| • Choose Information | | | | ✓ | | ✓ | | ✓ | ✓ | ✓ |
| • Construct | | | | | | | | | | |
| • Apply What Is Learned | ✓ | | | | | ✓ | | ✓ | ✓ | ✓ |
| **LEVEL 4 Analysing** | | | | | | | | | | |
| • Discriminate | | | ✓ | | ✓ | | ✓ | ✓ | | ✓ |
| • Illustrate | | | | | | | ✓ | | ✓ | ✓ |
| • Identify Relationships | | | | | | ✓ | ✓ | | | |
| **LEVEL 5 Evaluating** | | | | | | | | | | |
| • Decide | | | | | | | ✓ | | ✓ | ✓ |
| • Make Choices | | | | ✓ | ✓ | | | | ✓ | ✓ |
| **LEVEL 6 Creating** | | | | | | | | | | |
| • Design (i.e., a picture book) | | | | | | | | | ✓ | ✓ |
| • Create | | | | | | | | | ✓ | ✓ |

*Based on Bloom's Taxonomy*

# Contents

● ● ● ● ● ● ● ● ● ● ● ● ● ● ● ● ● ●

✔ **6 BONUS** Activity Pages! **Additional worksheets for your students**
✔ **6 BONUS** Overhead Transparencies! **For use with your projection system**

**FREE!**

- Go to our website: **www.classroomcompletepress.com/bonus**
- Enter item CC1111 or Word Families - Long Vowels
- Enter pass code CC1111D for Activity Pages. CC1111A for Overheads.

# Assessment Rubric

## Word Families - Long Vowels Grade K-1

Student's Name: _____  Assignment: _____  Level: _____

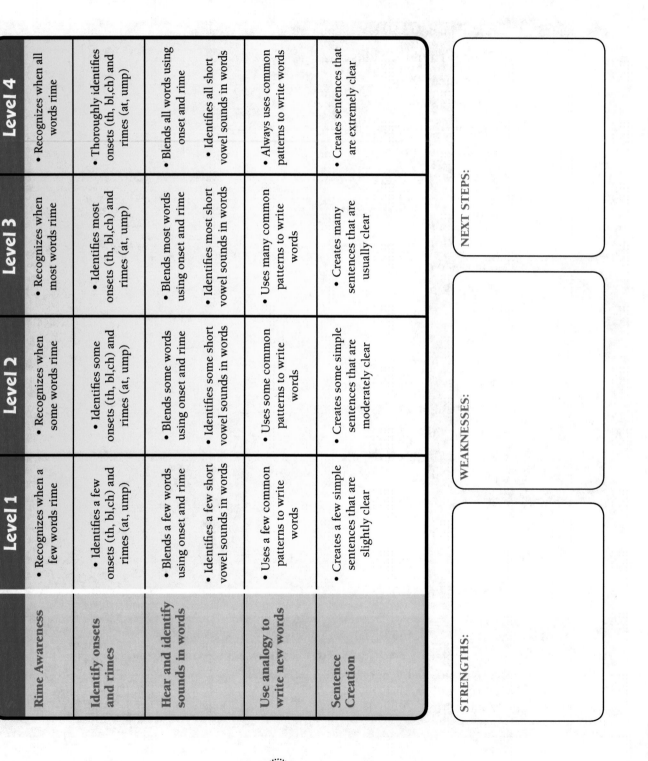

| | Level 1 | Level 2 | Level 3 | Level 4 |
|---|---|---|---|---|
| **Rime Awareness** | • Recognizes when a few words rime | • Recognizes when some words rime | • Recognizes when most words rime | • Recognizes when all words rime |
| **Identify onsets and rimes** | • Identifies a few onsets (th, bl,ch) and rimes (at, ump) | • Identifies some onsets (th, bl,ch) and rimes (at, ump) | • Identifies most onsets (th, bl,ch) and rimes (at, ump) | • Thoroughly identifies onsets (th, bl,ch) and rimes (at, ump) |
| **Hear and identify sounds in words** | • Blends a few words using onset and rime<br>• Identifies a few short vowel sounds in words | • Blends some words using onset and rime<br>• Identifies some short vowel sounds in words | • Blends most words using onset and rime<br>• Identifies most short vowel sounds in words | • Blends all words using onset and rime<br>• Identifies all short vowel sounds in words |
| **Use analogy to write new words** | • Uses a few common patterns to write words | • Uses some common patterns to write words | • Uses many common patterns to write words | • Always uses common patterns to write words |
| **Sentence Creation** | • Creates a few simple sentences that are slightly clear | • Creates some simple sentences that are moderately clear | • Creates many sentences that are usually clear | • Creates sentences that are extremely clear |

**STRENGTHS:**

**WEAKNESSES:**

**NEXT STEPS:**

Word Families - Long Vowels CC1111

# Teacher Guide

## Our resource has been created for ease of use by both TEACHERS and STUDENTS alike.

### Introduction

**I**ncrease vocabulary, sight word recognition and comprehension as you help your students identify the correct pronunciation of long vowel phonograms (word families) using real life pictures as an aid. We also highlight high frequency words which encourage beginning skills for reading. As students begin to read and understand more about the onset and rime connection found in word families, they will begin to think of words as not only a series of individual letters and sounds, but as easily recognizable segments or chunks of language. Reproducible work sheets include, riming, writing, poetry, cloze sentences, riddles and chunking.

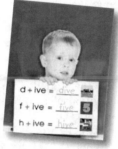

This resource provides ready-to-use information and activities for beginning readers. It can be used in any Language Arts program as a supplement to a balance literacy program to strengthen children's reading, writing and thinking skills.

Words are best learned in continuous text so you may wish to introduce the activities in this book as they appear in your shared reading, guided reading, writing and words blocks. This resource is comprised of interesting and engaging student activities in language, reading comprehension and writing, and can be effectively used for individual, small group or whole class activities.

### ONSETS

**Consonants:** s l p q n r t c k m b d f g h j v w x y z

**Consonant Blends:** bl cl fl gl pl sl tw br cr dr fr gr pr tr sc sk sm sn sp st sw gn gh gu kn wr sch scr shr spl spr str squ thr

**Consonant Digraphs:** ch kn ph qu sh th

### RIMES

| | | | | | | | | | |
|---|---|---|---|---|---|---|---|---|---|
| ail | ain | ake | ame | ank | ate | ay | eat | eep | eet |
| ice | ide | ime | ine | ive | ight | oat | oke | old | ole |
| one | ore | ose | y | | | | | | |

### How Is Our Resource Organized?

Activities in language, reading comprehension and writing (in the form of reproducible worksheets) make up the majority of our resource. There are a variety of pages organized in the following sections – PICTURE RIMES activities, BOXED WORDS activities, CLOZE activities, READING PASSAGE activities, and WRITING tasks. All are either a half-page or full page long.

It is not expected that all activities will be used, but are provided for variety and flexibility in the resource.

- Also provided are two puzzles, a word search and crossword. Each of these worksheets can be completed as individual activities or done in pairs.

- Three Graphic Organizers are included to help develop students' thinking and writing skills. The Assessment Rubric (page 4) is a useful tool for evaluating students' responses to many of the activities in our resource. The Comprehension Quiz (page 48) can be used for either a follow-up review or assessment at the completion of the unit.

**EASY MARKING™ ANSWER KEY**
Marking students' worksheets is fast and easy with our **Answer Key**. Answers are listed in columns – just line up the column with its corresponding worksheet, as shown, and see how every question matches up with its answer!

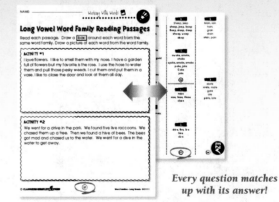

*Every question matches up with its answer!*

# 1,2,3,4,5,6
## Graphic Organizer Transparencies

Suggestions for using three of the six **Graphic Organizer Transparencies** included in our Word Family Book are found below. They may also be adapted to suit the individual needs of your students. The transparencies can be used on an overhead projector in teacher-led activities, and/or photocopied for use as student worksheets. To evaluate students' responses to any of the organizers, you may wish to use the **Assessment Rubric** (*on page 4*).

### ONSET-RIME CIRCLES

This organizer can be used as a whole class activity then as a small group or individual activity. **To introduce this to the whole class, place the small yellow circle of onsets inside the larger blue circle of rimes.** Not only will the students see that yellow and blue really do make green, they will also see how words can be made. Make a small whole in the center of each circle. Place a paper clip in the center and hold in place with a pencil. Spin both of the spinners. Add the onset to the rime. Say the word aloud. Ask the students: Does the word make sense? Does it sound right? Together determine if it is a real word. Record the real words on chart paper in a list. Then spin again. (For more advanced students, record the word on chart paper or the black board and ask: Does it look right?) After you have demonstrated how to use the onset-rime circles move the activity to a center for small groups or individual students to use for practice. Found on Page 55.

### ONSET-RIME WORD CHAINS

This organizer can be used as a whole class or small group activity. Divide the class into three groups. Give each group either a consonant, consonant blend or a consonant digraph. Either create your own or use the set provided on pages 44 & 45. Copy the onset cards on three different colors of colored cardstock (i.e. consonant digraphs – orange, consonant blends – green and consonants - blue) so that you know at a glance who has which onset. Give the students whom need additional support to be successful the consonants and those who can handle a challenge the digraphs. Select a rime and ask students to decide if their onset makes a real word when added to the rime. If their onset makes a real word, record it in the appropriate column. This activity gives students practice blending onsets and rimes and in distinguishing between consonants, blends and digraphs. Found on Page 56.

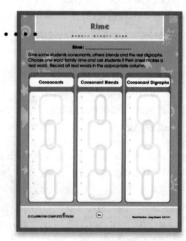

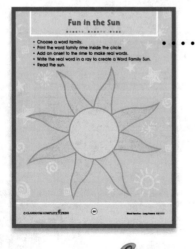

### FUN IN THE SUN

This organizer can be used as a whole class or an individual activity. For a class activity, lead your students in a brainstorming session. Record all of the word families that they know on the board. Choose one word family to make into a sun by adding onsets to the rime to create real words. As an individual activity, give students a copy of the overhead or make a sun with a round shape on top and print a word family, such as, "-ain" , inside the circle. Cut out ray shapes to be added to the sun. Students take a blank "ray," write a real word from the word family e.g. "rain". Each word gets added around the center to make a Word Family Sun. Substitute the word family and create other Word Family Suns. Extend the activity by having students write sentences using the words. Found on Page 58.

## Bloom's Taxonomy* for Reading Comprehension

The activities in this resource engage and build the full range of thinking skills that are essential for students' reading comprehension. Based on the six levels of thinking in Bloom's Taxonomy, questions are given that challenge students to not only recall what they have read, but move beyond this to understand the text through higher-order thinking. By using higher-order skills of applying, analysing, evaluating and creating, students become active readers, drawing more meaning from the text, and applying and extending their learning in more sophisticated ways.

Our **Word Families - Long Vowel Book**, therefore, is an effective tool for any Language Arts program. Whether it is used in whole or in part, or adapted to meet individual student needs, this resource provides teachers with the important questions to ask, inspiring students' interest, creativity, and promoting meaningful learning.

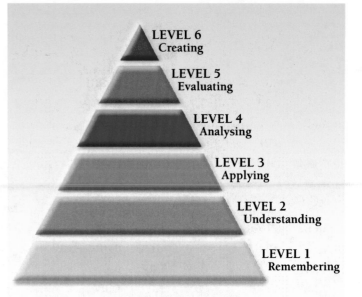

**BLOOM'S TAXONOMY:
6 LEVELS OF THINKING**

*Bloom's Taxonomy is a widely used tool by educators for classifying learning objectives, and is based on the work of Benjamin Bloom.*

# Dolch Sight Words

| GRADE PreK | | | | GRADE K | | | | GRADE 1 | | | |
|---|---|---|---|---|---|---|---|---|---|---|---|
| a | hers | **play** | | all | four | out | this | after | had | open | when |
| and | I | red | | am | get | please | too | again | has | over | |
| **away** | in | run | | are | good | pretty | under | an | her | put | |
| big | is | said | | at | has | ran | want | any | him | round | |
| blue | it | see | | **ate** | he | **ride** | was | as | how | some | |
| can | jump | the | | be | into | saw | well | ask | just | stop | |
| come | little | three | | black | like | **say** | went | **by** | know | **take** | |
| down | look | to | | brown | must | she | what | could | let | **thank** | |
| find | **make** | two | | but | new | so | white | every | **live** | them | |
| for | me | up | | **came** | no | soon | who | **fly** | **may** | then | |
| funny | **my** | we | | did | now | that | will | from | of | think | |
| go | not | yellow | | do | on | there | with | give | **old** | walk | |
| help | one | you | | **eat** | our | they | yes | going | once | where | |

# Vocabulary

## -ail
| | | |
|---|---|---|
| bail | nail | wail |
| fail | pail | frail |
| hail | rail | quail |
| jail | sail | snail |
| mail | tail | trail |

## -ain
| | |
|---|---|
| gain | chain |
| main | drain |
| pain | grain |
| rain | stain |
| brain | train |

## -ake
| | | |
|---|---|---|
| bake | take | snake |
| cake | wake | stake |
| lake | brake | |
| make | flake | |
| rake | shake | |

## -ame
| | |
|---|---|
| came | same |
| fame | tame |
| game | blame |
| lame | flame |

## -ank
| | | |
|---|---|---|
| bank | clank | thank |
| rank | crank | |
| sank | flank | |
| tank | plank | |
| blank | spank | |

## -ate
| | |
|---|---|
| fate | crate |
| gate | plate |
| late | skate |
| mate | state |

## -ay
| | | |
|---|---|---|
| bay | lay | way | sway |
| cay | may | away | tray |
| day | pay | clay |
| gay | ray | play |
| hay | say | stay |

## -eat
| | |
|---|---|
| beat | seat |
| heat | treat |
| meat | wheat |
| neat | |

## -eep
| | | |
|---|---|---|
| beep | peep | sleep |
| deep | creep | steep |
| jeep | weep | sweep |
| keep | sheep | |

## -eet
| | |
|---|---|
| beet | sheet |
| feet | sleet |
| meet | sweet |
| fleet | |

## -ice
| | |
|---|---|
| dice | price |
| lice | slice |
| mice | spice |
| nice | twice |
| rice | |

## -ide
| | |
|---|---|
| hide | bride |
| ride | glide |
| side | pride |
| tide | slide |
| wide | |

## -ime
| | |
|---|---|
| dime | crime |
| lime | prime |
| mime | |
| rime | |
| time | |

## -ine
| | |
|---|---|
| dine | pine |
| fine | tine |
| line | vine |
| mine | shine |
| nine | twine |

## -ive
| |
|---|
| dive |
| five |
| hive |
| live |
| drive |

## -ight
| | |
|---|---|
| fight | sight |
| light | tight |
| might | bright |
| night | fright |
| right | |

## -oat
| | |
|---|---|
| boat | gloat |
| coat | throat |
| goat | |
| bloat | |
| float | |

## -oke
| | | |
|---|---|---|
| Coke | awoke | stoke |
| joke | broke | stroke |
| poke | choke | |
| woke | smoke | |
| yoke | spoke | |

## -old
| | |
|---|---|
| bold | sold |
| cold | told |
| gold | |
| hold | |
| mold | |

## -ole
| |
|---|
| hole |
| mole |
| pole |
| stole |
| whole |

## -one
| | |
|---|---|
| bone | stone |
| cone | |
| tone | |
| zone | |
| phone | |

## -ore
| | | |
|---|---|---|
| bore | tore | snore |
| core | wore | store |
| more | chore | |
| pore | score | |
| sore | shore | |

## -ose
| |
|---|
| hose |
| nose |
| rose |
| close |
| those |

## -y
| | |
|---|---|
| by | sky |
| my | sly |
| cry | try |
| fly | why |
| ply | |

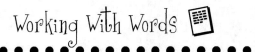 

# Onset – Rime Addition

**1.** Add the onset to the rime to create a new word. Say the word. Write the word on the line. **The first one has been done for you.**

> **sk + ate = skate**
>
> g + ate = _____
>
> l + ate = _____
>
> m + ate = _____
>
> cr + ate = _____
>
> pl + ate = _____
>
> f + ate = _____
>
> st + ate = _____

**2.** Write two sentences using the **–ate** family words.

a) _____

b) _____

# Onset – Rime Addition

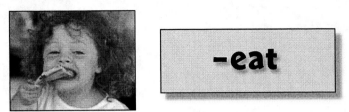

**-eat**

1. Add the onset to the rime to create a new word.   Say the word. Write the word on the line. **The first one has been done for you.**

_ + **eat** = **eat**

b + eat = _____

h + eat = _____

m + eat = _____

n + eat = _____

s + eat = _____

tr + eat = _____

wh + eat = _____

2. Write two sentences using the **–eat** family words.

a) _____

b) _____

# Onset – Rime Addition

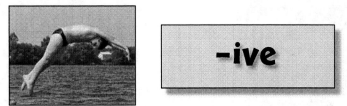

## -ive

**1.** Add the onset to the rime to create a new word.   Say the word. Write the word on the line. **The first one has been done for you.**

**d + ive = dive**

f + ive = _____

h + ive = _____

l + ive = _____

dr + ive = _____

**2.** Write three sentences using the **–ive** family words.

a) _____

b) _____

c) _____

# Onset - Rime Addition

-old

1. Add the onset to the rime to create a new word.   Say the word.
Write the word on the line. **The first one has been done for you.**

s + old = sold

b + old = _____

c + old = _____

g + old = _____

h + old = _____

m + old = _____

_ + old = _____

t + old = _____

2. Write two sentences using the **–old** family words.

a) _____

b) _____

# Onset – Rime Addition

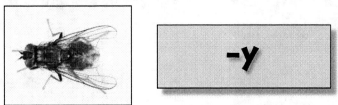

**-y**

**1.** Add the onset to the rime to create a new word.  Say the word.
Write the word on the line. **The first one has been done for you.**

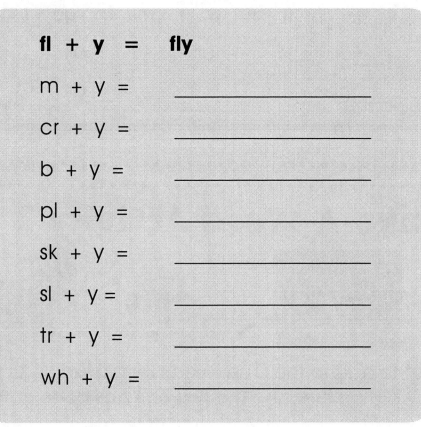

fl + y =    **fly**

m + y = _____

cr + y = _____

b + y = _____

pl + y = _____

sk + y = _____

sl + y = _____

tr + y = _____

wh + y = _____

**2.** Write two sentences using the **–y** family words.

a) _____

b) _____

# Make-A-Word Activity 1

-ail

Choose an onset to add to the rime to create a new word. Say the word. Write the word on the line. **The first one has been done for you.**

h   b   t   l   s   ~~sn~~   j   tr   n   p   r   m   fr   qu   f   w   cr

**sn**ail        ___ail        ___ail        ___ail        ___ail

___ail        ___ail        ___ail        ___ail        ___ail

___ail        ___ail        ___ail        ___ail        ___ail

# Make-A-Word Activity 2

-ame

Choose an onset to add to the rime to create a new word. Say the word. Write the word on the line. **The first one has been done for you.**

b   f   s   t   cr   l   ~~fl~~   bl   c   g

**fl**ame        ___ame        ___ame

___ame        ___ame        ___ame

___ame        ___ ___ame

Name: _____  Working With Words

# Make-A-Word Activity 3

## -ake

Choose an onset to add to the rime to create a new word. Say the word. Write the word on the line. **The first one has been done for you.**

h   b   t   l   s   st   c   sh   ~~sn~~   r   m   fl   br   w   cr

**sn**ake      ___ake      ___ake      ___ake      ___ake

___ake      ___ake      ___ake      ___ake      ___ake

___ake      ___ ___ake      ___ ___ake

# Make-A-Word Activity 4

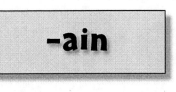

## -ain

Choose an onset to add to the rime to create a new word. Say the word. Write the word on the line. **The first one has been done for you.**

m   b   g   s   st   ch   p   br   ~~tr~~   r   gr   dr   sn

**tr**ain      ___ain      ___ain      ___ain

___ain      ___ain      ___ain      ___ain

___ ___ain      ___ ___ain

© CLASSROOM COMPLETE PRESS

15

**Word Families - Long Vowels CC1111**

# Make-A-Word Activity 5

-ank

Choose an onset to add to the rime to create a new word. Say the word. Write the word on the line. **The first one has been done for you.**

cl  b  t  l  s  str  r  sp  bl  th  pl  fl  cr

<u>t</u>ank     ___ank     ___ank     _____ank

___ank     ___ ___ank     ___ ___ank     ___ ___ank

___ank     ___ ___ank     ___ ___ank

# Make-A-Word Activity 6

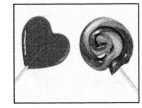 

-eet

Choose an onset to add to the rime to create a new word. Say the word. Write the word on the line. **The first one has been done for you.**

b  sl  d  f  t  cr  m  ~~sw~~  str  sh  fl

<u>sw</u>eet     ___eet     ___eet

___eet     ___eet     ___ ___eet

___ ___eet     ___eet

# Make-A-Word Activity 7

## -ice

Choose an onset to add to the rime to create a new word. Say the word. Write the word on the line. **The first one has been done for you.**

r  d  l  c  t  sp  m  st  tw  sl  n  pr

<u>d</u>ice          ___ice          ___ice

___ice          ___ice          ___ ___ice

___ ___ice          ___ ___ice          ___ ___ice

# Make-A-Word Activity 8

## -ime

Choose an onset to add to the rime to create a new word. Say the word. Write the word on the line. **The first one has been done for you.**

h  l  r  t  fl  m  pr  d  cr

<u>d</u>ime          ___ime          ___ime          ___ime

___ime          ___ ___ime          ___ ___ime

# Make-A-Word Activity 9

                              **-ine**

Choose an onset to add to the rime to create a new word. Say the word. Write the word on the line. **The first one has been done for you.**

d  n  b  p  sh  l  v  st  tw  f  m

**n**ine            ___ine            ___ine            ___ine

___ine            ___ine            ___ine

___ ___ine            ___ ___ine

# Make-A-Word Activity 10

                              **-ight**

Choose an onset to add to the rime to create a new word. Say the word. Write the word on the line. **The first one has been done for you.**

s  l  d  t  r  br  m  st  f  fr  n

**l**ight            ___ight            ___ight            ___ight

___ight            ___ight            ___ight

___ ___ight            ___ ___ight

NAME: _____

# Make-A-Word Activity 11

### -oke

Choose an onset to add to the rime to create a new word. Say the word. Write the word on the line. **The first one has been done for you.**

p ~~sm~~ w y j str ch C st fl br m sp aw

smoke ___oke ___oke ___oke
___oke ___oke ___oke ___oke
___oke ___oke ___oke ___oke

# Make-A-Word Activity 12

### -ore

Choose an onset to add to the rime to create a new word. Say the word. Write the word on the line. **The first one has been done for you.**

V ~~st~~ b p t cr m sn sh w sc c

store ___ore ___ore ___ore
___ore ___ore ___ore
___ore ___ore ___ore

# Long "a" Picture Rimes

Look at the picture. Choose the best onset to finish each word.

_____ake

_____ay

_____ame

_____ake

_____ail

_____ _____ame

_____ank

_____ _____ate

_____ _____ain

NAME: _____

# Long "e" Picture Rimes

Look at the picture. Choose the best onset to finish each word.

_____ _____eat

_____eep

_____eet

_____ _____eep

_____eep

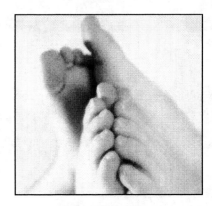
_____eet

_____at

_____eep

_____ _____eat

**Word Families - Long Vowels CC1111**

# Long "i" Picture Rimes

Look at the picture. Choose the best onset to finish each word.

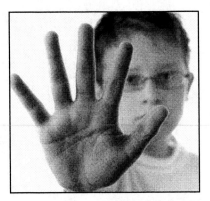

_____ive

_____ive

_____ice

_____ime

_____ide

_____ice

_____ine

_____ime

_____ight

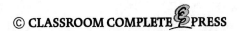

# Long "o" Picture Rimes

Look at the picture. Choose the best onset to finish each word.

\_\_\_\_\_oat

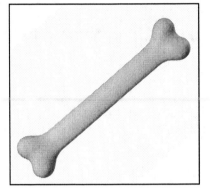

\_\_\_\_\_one

\_\_\_\_\_ose

\_\_\_\_\_old

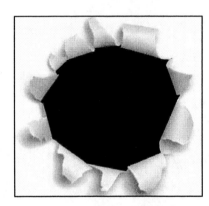

\_\_\_\_ \_\_\_\_\_ore

\_\_\_\_\_ole

\_\_\_\_ \_\_\_\_\_oke

\_\_\_\_\_ose

\_\_\_\_\_ose

 Working With Words

NAME: _____

# Long Vowel Sentence Completion

Choose a word from the box to make the sentence complete. The boxes show tall and small letters. **The first one has been done for you.**

May  ate  ~~rake~~  boat  eat  plate  try  came  bay  my  bank  cry  wheat

1. We ┌─┐┌─┐┌─┐┌─┐ **r** **a** **k** **e** the leaves in the fall.

2. ☐☐☐ I put my ☐☐☐☐ in the ☐☐☐ ?

3. I ☐☐☐ a ☐☐☐☐ of fries.

4. They ☐☐☐☐ over to ☐☐ house.

5. Mom went to the ☐☐☐☐ .

6. I ☐☐☐ not to ☐☐☐ when I am sad.

7. He likes to ☐☐☐ whole ☐☐☐☐☐ bread.

© CLASSROOM COMPLETE PRESS

24

**Word Families - Long Vowels CC1111**

# Long Vowel Sentence Completion

Choose a word from the box to make the sentence complete. The boxes show tall and small letters. **The first one has been done for you.**

| stain | bright | bake | ~~sweep~~ | feet | cake | ~~keep~~ | beet | light | nice | slice | Coke |

**1.** You must | s | w | e | e | p | to | k | e | e | p | the floor clean.

**2.** My mom wants me to ☐☐☐ a ☐☐☐ .

**3.** Joe got a ☐☐☐☐☐ on his pants.

**4.** The ☐☐☐☐ fell on his ☐☐☐ .

**5.** Can I have a can of ☐☐☐☐ ?

**6.** The ☐☐☐☐ man gave me a ☐☐☐☐☐ of cake.

**7.** The ☐☐☐☐☐☐ ☐☐☐☐☐ woke him up.

**Word Families - Long Vowels CC1111**

# Long Vowel Sentence Completion

Choose a word from the box to make the sentence complete. The boxes show tall and small letters. **The first one has been done for you.**

five   dive   time   dime   pine   drive   cold   nine   stone   ~~store~~   ~~hose~~   hide

1. She went to the   s t o r e   today to buy a

   h o s e .

2. Mom gave me ☐☐☐☐ dollars and a

   ☐☐☐☐ to buy a pop.

3. Take the ☐☐☐☐ to learn how to

   ☐☐☐☐☐ safely.

4. I saw ☐☐☐☐ ☐☐☐☐ trees on my walk.

5. He doesn't like to ☐☐☐☐ when the water is

   ☐☐☐☐ .

6. She likes to ☐☐☐☐ in the ☐☐☐☐☐ pile.

# -ake Cloze

Choose the best word to finish each sentence. Say the word in the sentence. If it sounds right and makes sense, write the word on the line. **The first one has been done for you.**

~~shake~~ bake  lake  wake  rake  take  snake  make  brake

1. He likes to **shake** and _____.

2. Can you _____ my mom?

3. My dad likes to swim in the _____.

4. She had to _____ a _____ to the garden.

5. He has a pet _____.

6. The horse and buggy had to _____ for the car.

7. I want to _____ some cookies for my class.

NAME: _____

# -ay Cloze

Choose the best word to finish each sentence. Say the word in the sentence. If it sounds right and makes sense, write the word on the line. **The first one has been done for you.**

~~tray~~   way   May   bay   play   say   hay   pay   day   stay   away

1. Get a **tray** for our food.  I will _____.

2. _____ I come to your house and _____?

3. Which _____ is it to the _____?

4. We like to jump in the _____.

5. He went _____ to school..

6. I want to _____ and play all _____.

7. What did you _____?

# -ame Cloze

Choose the best word to finish each sentence. Say the word in the sentence. If it sounds right and makes sense, write the word on the line. **The first one has been done for you.**

| came | tame | same | game | lame | blame | fame | ~~flame~~ |

1. The **flame** in the fire is very hot.

2. We _____ together to school.

3. This lamb is _____ and sick.

4. We long for _____ and fortune.

5. We have the _____ taste in clothes.

6. We lost our soccer _____ and I am to _____.

7. I want to _____ a tiger.

NAME: _____

# -ide Cloze

Choose the best word to finish each sentence. Say the word in the sentence. If it sounds right and makes sense, write the word on the line. **The first one has been done for you.**

glide  ~~slide~~  hide  ride  side  pride  slide  wide  bride

1. Let's go down the **slide**.

2. Lions live together in a _____.

3. We like to go down the _____ yellow _____.

4. My aunt is going to be a _____.

5. Let's play _____ and seek.

6. I slept on the left _____ of the bed.

7. I like the _____ _____ at the park.

# -one Cloze

Choose the best word to finish each sentence. Say the word in the sentence. If it sounds right and makes sense, write the word on the line. **The first one has been done for you.**

| bone | cone | ~~tone~~ | zone | phone | stone | stone |

1. I need to **tone** my muscles.

2. The time _____ changes over the equator.

3. She threw a _____ in the water.

4. Joey got an ice cream _____ at the store.

5. He fell and broke his elbow _____.

6. Could you please answer the _____?

7. We have a _____ fire place.

NAME: _____

# -oat Cloze

Choose the best word to finish each sentence. Say the word in the sentence. If it sounds right and makes sense, write the word on the line. **The first one has been done for you.**

| boat | coat | goat | bloat | float | ~~gloat~~ | throat |
|------|------|------|-------|-------|-----------|--------|

**1.** He had to **gloat** when he won the race.

**2.** They have a big _____ in the bay.

**3.** I have a sore _____ .

**4.** The _____ ate the man's hat.

**5.** The fish _____ in the sea.

**6.** Can you _____ in the water?

**7.** I have a brown and white _____ .

# Find a Long Vowel Rime

1.  Read the sentences.  (Circle) all of the words that rime.

    **a)** I saw a snail on the trail on the way home.

    **b)** The rain went down the drain.

    **c)** Jake likes to make chocolate cake.

    **d)** They came and played the same game with us.

    **e)** The boat in my fish tank sank to the bottom.

    **f)** We arrived late to skate and the gate was shut.

    **g)** We like to play in the hay down by the bay.

    **h)** Mom bought us a treat to beat the heat.

2.  Choose two word families. Write two sentences using the words.

    **a)** _____

    _____

    **b)** _____

    _____

# Find a Long Vowel Rime

1. Read the sentences. (Circle) all of the words that rime.

   **a)** I have a treat made from wheat.

   **b)** The Jeep went beep, beep as it went down the steep hill.

   **c)** My feet got very sore as I walked on the street.

   **d)** I paid a big price for the new spice.

   **e)** We like to glide down the wide slide.

   **f)** Mom gave me a dime to buy a lime.

   **g)** Can I drive to the dive with you?

   **h)** I put a coat of paint on my boat.

2. Choose two word families. Write two sentences using the words.

   **a)** _____

   _____

   **b)** _____

   _____

# Find a Long Vowel Rime

1. Read the sentences. (Circle) all of the words that rime.

   **a)** Why does my brother always cry?

   **b)** The mole got stuck in the hole.

   **c)** I smell the rose with my nose.

   **d)** The stone hit my bone.

   **e)** I was told that you sold gold.

   **f)** The birds fly by my house.

   **g)** The tone on my phone is funny.

   **h)** The goat ate my dad's coat.

2. Choose two word families. Write two sentences using the words.

   **a)** _____

   _____

   **b)** _____

   _____

*Working With Words*   NAME: _____

# Long Vowel Word Family Reading Passages

Read each passage.  Draw a box around each word from the
same word family. Draw a picture of each word from the word family.

## ACTIVITY #1

The sheep walked along the road.  They found a jeep. The sheep
jumped into the jeep. The horn went beep! Beep! It went down
a steep hill and hit a deep hole. It was in a big heap. The sheep
began to weep. They all went to sleep.

## ACTIVITY #2

I awoke to smell the smoke.  I started to choke.  Help! Help! I
spoke louder and louder.  Smoke! Smoke!  My brother gave me a
poke and said it was all a joke.  He burned the toast. He handed
me a Coke. I was not very happy with his joke.

# Long Vowel Word Family Reading Passages

Read each passage. Draw a box around each word from the same word family. Draw a picture of each word from the word family.

## ACTIVITY #1

I love flowers. I like to smell them with my nose. I have a garden full of flowers but my favorite is the rose. I use the hose to water them and pull those pesky weeds. I cut them and put them in a vase. I like to close the door and look at them all day.

## ACTIVITY #2

We went for a drive in the park. We found five live raccoons. We chased them up a tree. Then we found a hive of bees. The bees got mad and chased us to the water. We went for a dive in the water to get away.

# Long Vowel Word Family Reading Passages

Read each passage. Draw a | box | around each word from the same word family. Draw a picture of each word from the word family.

## ACTIVITY #1

I live on Main Street. I love the rain on warm days when the train goes by. The water splashes in the field on the grain. I like to watch the water go down the street and into the drain. Once I fell and got a stain on my pants. I also got a pain in my knee.

## ACTIVITY #2

Our dog likes to skate with us on the ice. He slides around on a crate that my mate made. We push him through the gate in our yard. We laugh and laugh. After we went in the house and ate cookies on a silver plate. We had so much fun that my dad was late for work.

# What's different?

(Circle) the word that is from a different word family.

| | | | | |
|---|---|---|---|---|
| **1.** | rake | bail | fail | mail |
| **2.** | gain | chain | bank | stain |
| **3.** | make | sank | cake | take |
| **4.** | flame | lame | play | blame |
| **5.** | black | bank | plank | crank |
| **6.** | mate | gate | skate | same |
| **7.** | by | bay | play | stay |
| **8.** | beat | hat | heat | meat |
| **9.** | sheep | keep | rep | sleep |
| **10.** | seat | feet | sweet | street |

Choose two different word families not shown above. Write three words from each of the word families below.

_____     _____     _____

_____     _____     _____

# Writing Task #1: Song Composition

**ACTIVITY #1**    Choose a rime from the rime cards.  Use the onset cards to create as many words as you can.  Rime: _____

_____        _____        _____

_____        _____        _____

**ACTIVITY #2**

Use the words to compose a song.

_____

_____

_____

_____

_____

_____

_____

_____

_____

_____

# Writing Task #2: Riming Poem

**ACTIVITY #1**   Choose a rime from the rime cards.  Use the onset cards to create as many words as you can.

Rime: _____

_____    _____    _____

_____    _____    _____

_____    _____    _____

_____    _____    _____

## ACTIVITY #2

Use the words to compose a poem.

_____

by _____

_____

_____

_____

_____

_____

_____

NAME: _____

# Rime Cards

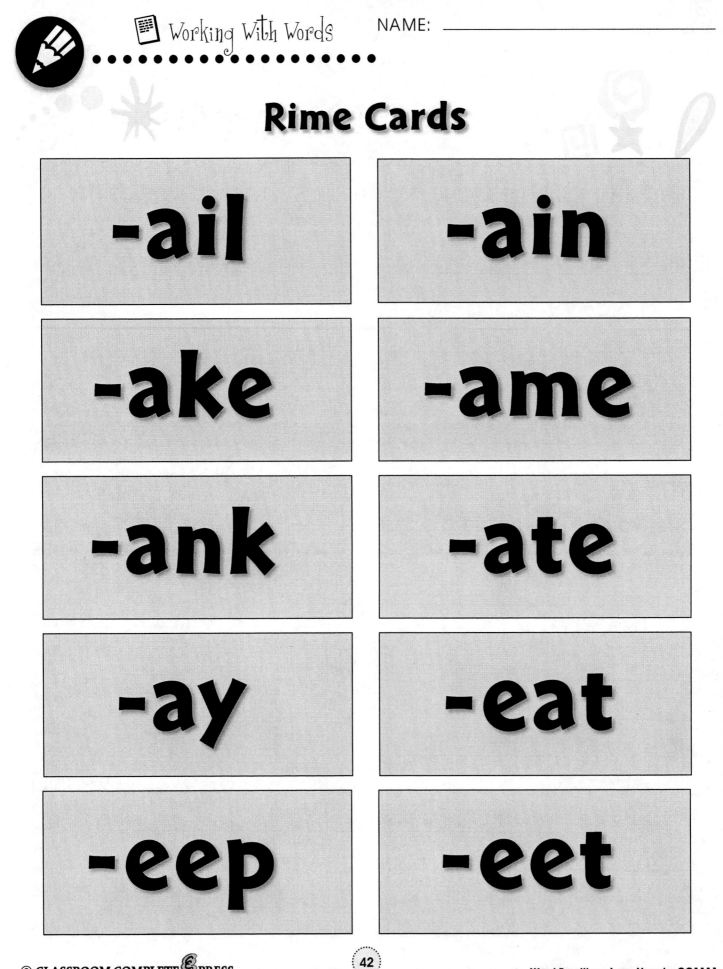

| -ail | -ain |
| -ake | -ame |
| -ank | -ate |
| -ay | -eat |
| -eep | -eet |

# Rime Cards

| | |
|---|---|
| -ine | -ime |
| -ive | -ight |
| -oat | -oke |
| -old | -ole |
| -one | -ore |

# Onset Cards

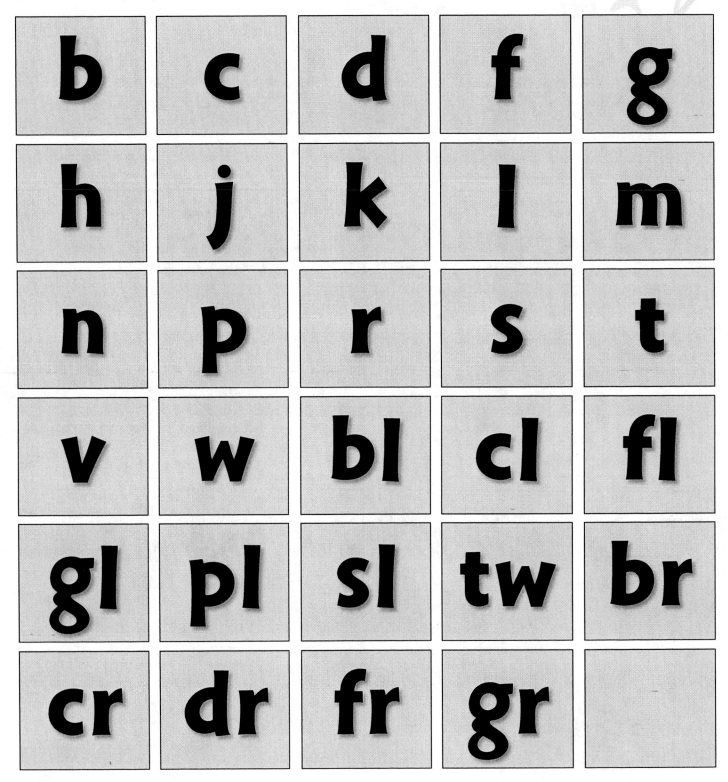

| | | | | |
|---|---|---|---|---|
| b | c | d | f | g |
| h | j | k | l | m |
| n | p | r | s | t |
| v | w | bl | cl | fl |
| gl | pl | sl | tw | br |
| cr | dr | fr | gr | |

Working With Words

# Onset Cards

| | | | | |
|---|---|---|---|---|
| pr | tr | sc | sk | sm |
| sn | sp | st | sw | gn |
| gu | kn | wr | ch | sh |
| th | qu | ph | squ | thr |
| shr | str | scr | spl | sch |
| | | | | |

MY NAME: _____

# Crossword Puzzle

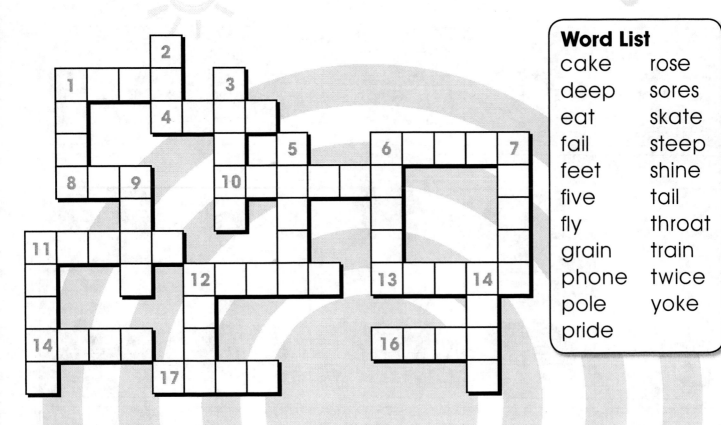

**Word List**

| cake | rose |
| --- | --- |
| deep | sores |
| eat | skate |
| fail | steep |
| feet | shine |
| five | tail |
| fly | throat |
| grain | train |
| phone | twice |
| pole | yoke |
| pride | |

## Across

1. to lose
4. the yellow part of an egg
6. bandaids cover
8. to gobble
10. in your neck
11. carries people and cargo
12. used to call people
13. where lions live
14. you bake and ice this
16. a red flower
17. you use these to walk

## Down

1. one, two, three, four, …
2. what a bird can do
3. a sport on ice
5. used to make bread
6. vertical hills
7. the car has a bright _____
9. a dog has a furry one
11. two times
12. used to fish
14. the water is this when you dive

Word Families - Long Vowels CC1111

☳☳ Hands-On Activities
• • • • • • • • • • • • • • • • • • •

# Word Search

**Find all of the words in the Word Search. Words are written horizontally, vertically, diagonally, and some are even written backwards.**

| bank | broke | cold | lake | side | tone | wide |
|------|-------|------|------|------|------|------|
| bay | chain | creep | meet | sky | twice | |
| beet | choke | five | nice | snail | wake | |
| bride | close | game | nose | store | wheat | |
| bright | coat | hole | pine | thank | why | |

| s | x | p | q | z | s | f | t | h | g | i | r | b | h | a | e |
|---|---|---|---|---|---|---|---|---|---|---|---|---|---|---|---|
| n | i | c | e | i | l | i | a | n | c | c | q | a | e | i | n |
| a | v | a | k | c | e | r | e | v | i | f | l | a | d | t | i |
| i | a | g | a | d | o | e | h | o | h | s | p | o | i | r | p |
| l | c | b | i | n | t | f | w | w | s | t | m | p | s | o | r |
| a | j | r | p | i | d | t | g | h | o | l | e | s | k | e | a |
| m | b | a | e | e | e | b | a | y | y | e | e | e | e | k | b |
| c | e | c | w | e | d | r | a | y | a | n | t | r | e | o | r |
| o | o | k | b | d | p | o | a | l | l | t | g | u | b | h | c |
| n | o | a | w | h | e | k | z | o | b | h | t | w | i | c | e |
| o | t | d | t | t | r | e | j | l | u | a | i | p | e | w | r |
| s | k | y | o | e | q | c | h | a | i | n | u | e | e | i | o |
| e | e | d | n | e | n | c | m | k | d | k | n | a | b | l | t |
| g | a | m | e | k | n | o | p | e | i | k | w | e | l | l | s |
| e | t | i | t | a | i | l | o | l | t | x | c | v | b | n | b |
| h | i | m | w | w | i | d | e | r | u | l | s | a | e | t | q |

MY NAME: _____

# Long Vowel Comprehension Quiz

**PART 1: MULTIPLE CHOICE**

(Circle) the answer that is correct.

**30**

1. Which word is not a long vowel word family rime?

   **a)** ate          **b)** is          **c)** eat          **1**

2. Which word does not belong?

   **a)** oat          **b)** hot          **c)** boat          **1**

3. Which onset makes a real word when added to the rime –old ?

   **a)** w          **b)** d          **c)** f          **1**

4. Which onset does not make a real word when added to the rime –ight?

   **a)** sc          **b)** s          **c)** sl          **1**

5. Which sentence has two long word family words?

   **a)** The sun is very hot.

   **b)** She ate a big cake.

   **c)** My mom went to Florida.

   **1**

**PART 2: TRUE OR FALSE**

(Circle) **T** if the statement is TRUE **or** **F** if it is FALSE.

**5**

T   F   **a)** "Fose" is a real word.

T   F   **b)** "Oat, old, and eat" are words and word family rimes.

T   F   **c)** "Seat, beet and neat" are all one word family.

T   F   **d)** The onsets, "p, m, t" make real words when added to the rime –ole.

T   F   **e)** The words "my, fly, cry" are all from the same word family.

**SUBTOTAL:          /10**

# Long Vowel Comprehension Quiz

**Answer the questions in complete sentences.**

**1.** Why do you think it is important to learn about word families?  ②

_____

_____

_____

**2.** Write a sentence using two long vowel word family words.  ②

_____

_____

_____

**3.** List five model words and draw a picture to represent each word.

| | | | | | ⑩ |
|---|---|---|---|---|---|

**4.** List three onsets.  ③

_____   _____   _____

**5.** List three rimes.  ③

_____   _____   _____

**SUBTOTAL:**   /20

**7.** dice, twice, rice, lice, spice, mice, slice, nice, price

**8.** dime, lime, rime, time, mime, prime, crime

(17)

**5.** tank, blank, clank, bank, sank, rank, spank, thank, plank, flank, crank

**6.** sweet, beet, sleet, feet, meet, street, sheet, fleet

(16)

**3.** snake, bake, take, lake, stake, cake, shake, rake, make, flake, brake, wake, sake

**4.** train, gain, main, stain, chain, pain, brain, rain, grain, drain

(15)

**1.** fly, my, cry, by, ply, sky, sly, try, why

**2.** Answers will vary.

(13)

**1.** snail, hail, bail, tail, sail, nail, jail, trail, pail, rail, mail, frail, quail, fail, wail

**2.** flame, fame, same, tame, lame, blame, came, game

(14)

**1.** dive, five, hive, live, drive

**2.** Answers will vary.

(11)

**1.** sold, bold, cold, gold, hold, mold, old, told

**2.** Answers will vary.

(12)

**1.** skate, gate, late, mate, crate, plate, fate, state

**2.** Answers will vary.

(9)

**1.** eat, beat, heat, meat, neat, seat, treat, wheat

**2.** Answers will vary.

(10)

**2.** bake, cake
**3.** stain
**4.** beet, feet
**5.** Coke
**6.** nice, slice
**7.** bright, light

25

**2.** May, boat, bay
**3.** ate, plate
**4.** came, my
**5.** bank
**6.** try, cry
**7.** eat, wheat

24

five
dive
dice

time
slide
mice

nine
dime
light

22

boat
bone
rose

sold
store
hole

smoke
nose
hose

23

rake
hay
game

cake
mail
flame

tank
skate
chain

20

wheat
jeep
beet

sweep
sheep
feet

eat
sleep
treat

21

**5.**
smoke
poke
woke
yoke
joke
stroke
choke
stoke
broke
spoke
awoke
Coke

**6.**
store
bore
pore
tore
more
snore
shore
wore
score
core

19

**5.**
nine
dine
line
pine
shine
vine
fine
mine
twine

**6.**
light
sight
fight
right
tight
bright
might
fright
night

18

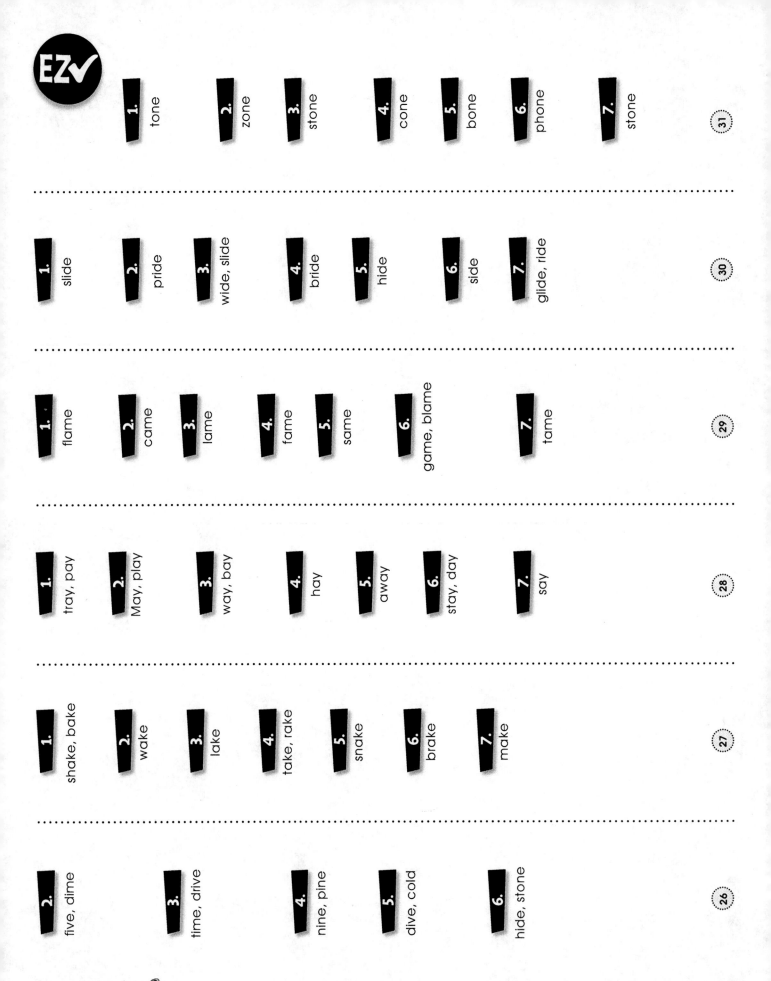

**1.** tone  **2.** zone  **3.** stone  **4.** cone  **5.** bone  **6.** phone  **7.** stone  (31)

**1.** slide  **2.** pride  **3.** wide, slide  **4.** bride  **5.** hide  **6.** side  **7.** glide, ride  (30)

**1.** flame  **2.** came  **3.** lame  **4.** fame  **5.** same  **6.** game, blame  **7.** tame  (29)

**1.** tray, pay  **2.** May, play  **3.** way, bay  **4.** hay  **5.** away  **6.** stay, day  **7.** say  (28)

**1.** shake, bake  **2.** wake  **3.** lake  **4.** take, rake  **5.** snake  **6.** brake  **7.** make  (27)

**2.** five, dime  **3.** time, drive  **4.** nine, pine  **5.** dive, cold  **6.** hide, stone  (26)

**1.** Main, rain
train,
grain
drain
stain, pain

**2.** skate
crate, mate
gate
ate
plate, late

(38)

**1.** Sheep, jeep
sheep, jeep, beep
Beep, steep, deep
sheep, weep
sleep

**2.** awoke, smoke,
choke
spoke, smoke, smoke
poke, joke
Coke
joke

(36)

**1.** nose
rose, hose, those
close

**2.** drive, five, live
hive
dive

(37)

**1.**
a) Why, my, cry
b) mole, hole
c) rose, nose
d) stone, bone
e) told, sold, gold
f) fly, by, my
g) tone, phone
h) goat, coat

**2.** Answers will vary.

(35)

**1.**
a) treat, wheat
b) Jeep, beep, beep, steep
c) feet, street
d) price, spice
e) glide, wide, slide
f) dime, lime
g) drive, dive
h) coat, boat

**2.** Answers will vary.

(34)

**1.**
a) snail, trail
b) rain, drain
c) Jake, make, cake
d) came, same, game
e) tank, sank
f) late, skate, gate
g) play, hay, bay
h) treat, beat, heat

**2.** Answers will vary.

(33)

**1.** gloat
**2.** boat
**3.** throat
**4.** goat
**5.** bloat
**6.** float
**7.** coat.

(32)

**1.** Answers will vary. Give two points if the student mentions that word families make reading and writing easier because you know a model word or pattern rather than having to sound out individual letters.

**2.** Answers will vary. Give one point for a complete sentence and one point for using two word families.

**3.** Answers will vary.

**4.** Answers will vary.

**5.** Answers will vary.

(49)

**1.** b)

**2.** b)

**3.** c)

**4.** a)

**5.** b)

**PART 2.**

a) F
b) T
c) F
d) F
e) T

(48)

**Across**
1. fall
4. yoke
6. sores
8. eat
10. throat
11. train
12. phone
13. pride
14. cake
16. rose
17. feet

**Down**
1. five
2. fly
3. skate
5. grain
6. steep
7. shine
9. tail
11. twice
12. pole
14. deep

(46)

## Word Search Answers

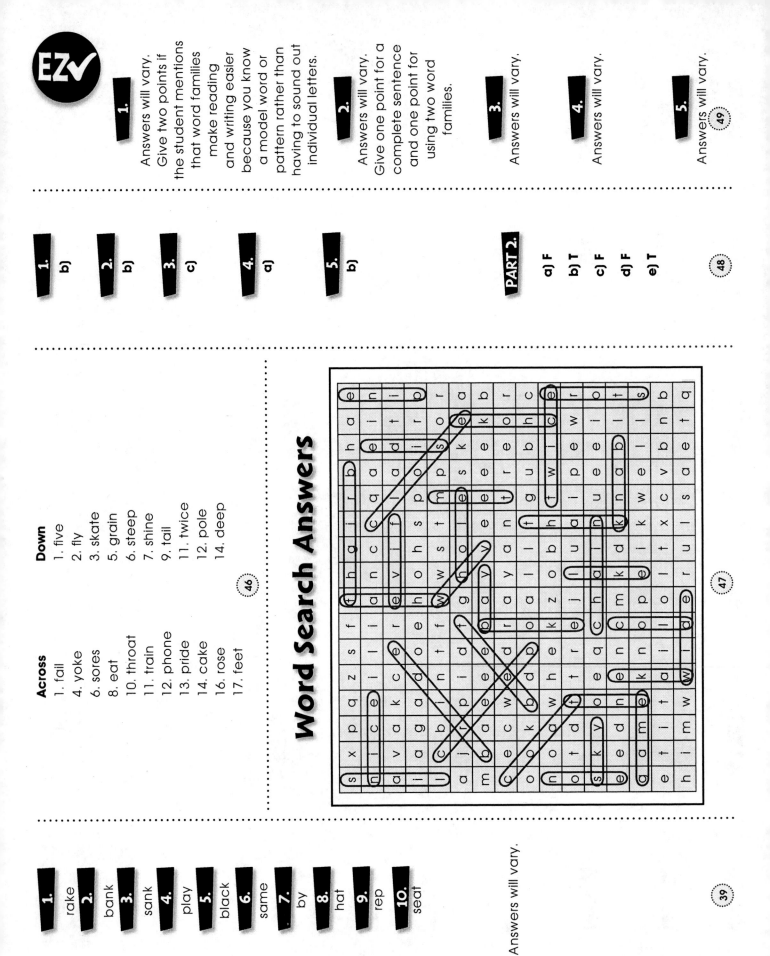

(47)

**1.** rake

**2.** bank

**3.** sank

**4.** play

**5.** black

**6.** same

**7.** by

**8.** hat

**9.** rep

**10.** seat

Answers will vary.

(39)

# Words We Know

● ● ● ● ● ● ● ● ● ● ● ● ● ● ● ● ● ● ●

# Words We Know

# Publication Listing

● ● ● ● ● ● ● ● ● ● ● ● ● ● ● ●

## Ask Your Dealer About Our Complete Line

### REGULAR EDUCATION
● ● ● ● ● ● ● ● ● ● ● ● ● ● ●

## REMEDIAL EDUCATION
Reading Level 3-4  Grades 5-8
● ● ● ● ● ● ● ● ● ● ● ● ● ● ● ● ● ●

## LANGUAGE ARTS

| ITEM # | TITLE |
|---|---|
| | **LITERACY SKILL SERIES** |
| CC1106 | Reading Response Forms: Grades 1-2 NEW! |
| CC1107 | Reading Response Forms Grades 3-4 NEW! |
| CC1108 | Reading Response Forms Grades 5-6 NEW! |
| CC1109 | Reading Response Forms Big Book NEW! |
| CC1110 | Word Families - Short Vowels: Grades K-1 NEW! |
| CC1111 | Word Families - Long Vowels: Grades K-1 NEW! |
| CC1112 | Word Families Big Book: Grades K-1 NEW! |
| | **LITERATURE KITS  GRADES 1-2** |
| CC2100 | Curious George (H. A. Rey) |
| CC2101 | Paper Bag Princess (Robert N. Munsch) |
| CC2102 | Stone Soup (Marcia Brown) |
| CC2103 | The Very Hungry Caterpillar (Eric Carle) |
| CC2104 | Where the Wild Things Are (Maurice Sendak) |
| | **LITERATURE KITS  GRADES 3-4** |
| CC2300 | Babe: The Gallant Pig (Dick King-Smith) |
| CC2301 | Because of Winn-Dixie (Kate DiCamillo) |
| CC2302 | The Tale of Despereaux (Kate DiCamillo) |
| CC2303 | James and the Giant Peach (Roald Dahl) |
| CC2304 | Ramona Quimby, Age 8 (Beverly Cleary) |
| CC2305 | The Mouse and the Motorcycle (Beverly Cleary) |
| CC2306 | Charlotte's Web (E.B. White) NEW! |
| CC2307 | Owls in the Family (Farley Mowat) NEW! |
| | **LITERATURE KITS  GRADES 5-6** |
| CC2500 | Black Beauty (Anna Sewell) |
| CC2501 | Bridge to Terabithia (Katherine Paterson) |
| CC2502 | Bud, Not Buddy (Christopher Paul Curtis) |
| CC2503 | The Egypt Game (Zilpha Keatley Snyder) |
| CC2504 | The Great Gilly Hopkins (Katherine Paterson) |
| CC2505 | Holes (Louis Sachar) |
| CC2506 | Number the Stars (Lois Lowry) |
| CC2507 | The Sign of the Beaver (E.G. Speare) |
| CC2508 | The Whipping Boy (Sid Fleischman) |
| CC2509 | Island of the Blue Dolphins (Scott O'Dell) NEW! |
| CC2510 | Underground to Canada (Barbara Smucker) NEW! |
| CC2511 | Loser (Jerry Spinelli) NEW! |
| | **LITERATURE KITS  GRADES 7-8** |
| CC2700 | Cheaper by the Dozen (Frank B. Gilbreth) NEW! |
| CC2701 | The Miracle Worker (William Gibson) NEW! |
| CC2702 | The Red Pony (John Steinbeck) NEW! |
| CC2703 | Treasure Island (Robert Louis Stevenson) NEW! |
| CC2704 | Romeo and Juliet (William Shakespeare) NEW! |

## SCIENCE

| ITEM # | TITLE |
|---|---|
| | **ECOLOGY & THE ENVIRONMENT SERIES** |
| CC4500 | Ecosystems |
| CC4501 | Classification & Adaptation |
| CC4502 | Cells |
| CC4503 | Ecology & The Environment Big Book |
| | **MATTER & ENERGY SERIES** |
| CC4504 | Properties of Matter |
| CC4505 | Atoms, Molecules & Elements |
| CC4506 | Energy |
| CC4507 | The Nature of Matter Big Book |
| | **HUMAN BODY SERIES** |
| CC4516 | Cells, Skeletal & Muscular Systems |
| CC4517 | Nervous, Senses & Respiratory Systems |
| CC4518 | Circulatory, Digestive Excretory & Reproductive |
| CC4519 | Human Body Big Book |
| | **FORCE & MOTION SERIES** |
| CC4508 | Force |
| CC4509 | Motion |
| CC4510 | Simple Machines |
| CC4511 | Force, Motion & Simple Machines Big Book |
| | **SPACE & BEYOND SERIES** |
| CC4512 | Space - Solar Systems |
| CC4513 | Space - Galaxies & The Universe |
| CC4514 | Space - Travel & Technology |
| CC4515 | Space Big Book |

## ENVIRONMENTAL STUDIES

| ITEM # | TITLE |
|---|---|
| | **MANAGING OUR WASTE SERIES** |
| CC5764 | Waste: At the Source |
| CC5765 | Prevention, Recycling & Conservation |
| CC5766 | Waste: The Global View |
| CC5767 | Waste Management Big Book |
| | **CLIMATE CHANGE SERIES** |
| CC5769 | Global Warming: Causes NEW! |
| CC5770 | Global Warming: Effects NEW! |
| CC5771 | Global Warming: Reduction NEW! |
| CC5772 | Global Warming Big Book NEW! |

## SOCIAL STUDIES

| ITEM # | TITLE |
|---|---|
| | **WORLD CONTINENTS SERIES** |
| CC5750 | North America |
| CC5751 | South America |
| CC5768 | The Americas Big Book |
| CC5752 | Europe |
| CC5753 | Africa |
| CC5754 | Asia |
| CC5755 | Australia |
| CC5756 | Antarctica |
| | **NORTH AMERICAN GOVERNMENT SERIES** |
| CC5757 | American Government |
| CC5758 | Canadian Government |
| CC5759 | Mexican Government |
| CC5760 | Governments of North America Big Book |
| | **WORLD GOVERNMENT SERIES** |
| CC5761 | World Political Leaders |
| CC5762 | World Electoral Processes NEW! |
| CC5763 | Capitalism versus Communism NEW! |
| CC5777 | World Politics Big Book NEW! |
| | **WORLD CONFLICT  SERIES** |
| CC5500 | American Civil War |
| CC5501 | World War I |
| CC5502 | World War II |
| CC5503 | World Wars I & II Big Book |
| CC5505 | Korean War NEW! |
| CC5506 | Vietnam War NEW! |
| CC5507 | Korean & Vietnam Wars Big Book NEW! |

VISIT:

## www.CLASSROOM COMPLETE 𝒫PRESS.com

To view sample pages from each book